LET'S GROW.

THIS BOOK IS DEDICATED TO MY SUNFLOWERS~

MY DAUGHTER, MY MOTHER, MY COUSINS AND AUNTS
WHO EACH CARRY A PIECE OF OUR BELOVED GRAMMY
WITHIN THEIR HEARTS.

TO ALL OF THE WOMEN OUT THERE
WHO HELP OTHERS GROW.

PLEASE REACH OUT TO BOOK A WORKSHOP OR AUTHOR VISIT

www.creativekindnessco.com

# Sunny

## A STORY OF LIFE & LOVE

WRITTEN & ILLUSTRATED BY TASSIA SCHREINER

ARTWORK COLLABORATION WITH ANHELINA STEPANOVA

HEY THERE, SUNNY,
WE ARE SO GLAD YOU
ARE HERE.

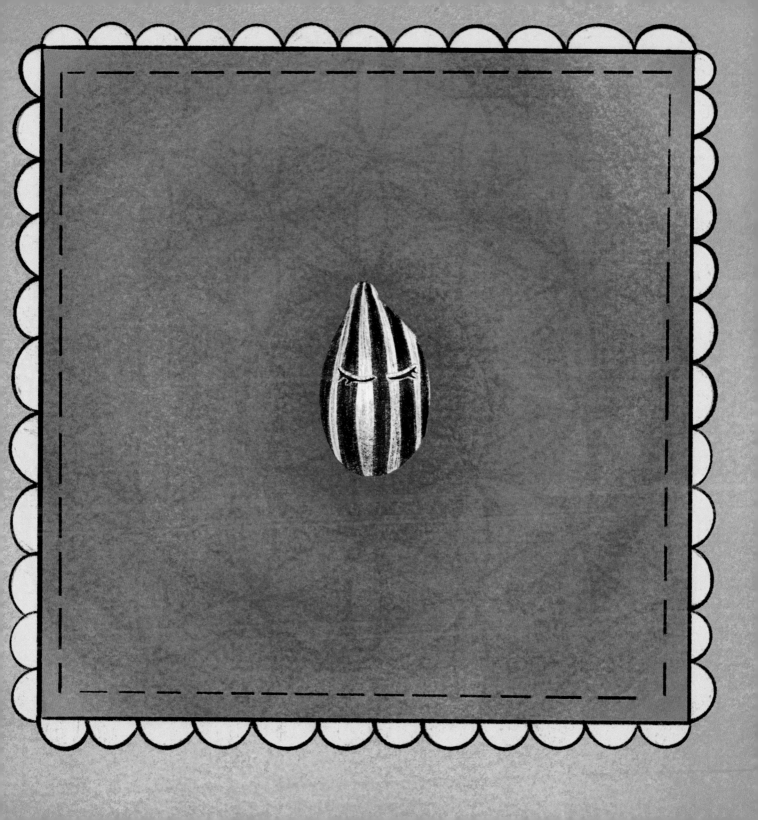

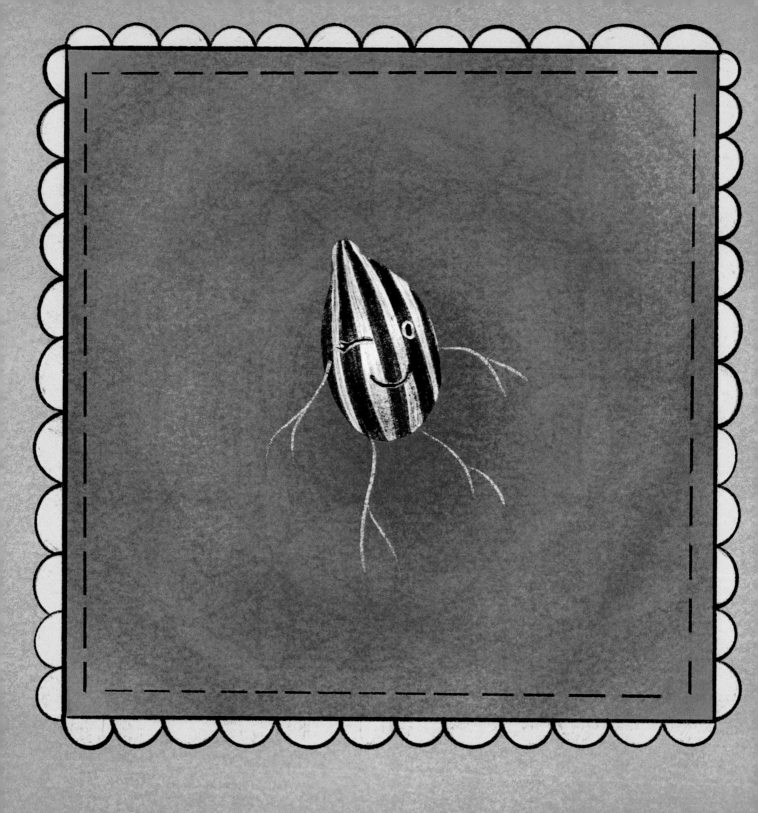

I KNOW YOU FEEL LITTLE,
BUT THE POTENTIAL
TUCKED WITHIN YOU
IS GREATER
THAN YOU COULD EVER IMAGINE.

WE WILL GIVE YOU A SAFE PLACE
TO LAY YOUR ROOTS—
GOOD FOOD, RICH IDEAS.
WE WILL NURTURE YOU

AS YOU GROW.

GROWING IS HARD.
IT WON'T ALWAYS BE EASY.
SOMETIMES YOU MIGHT FEEL
LIKE YOU ARE GOING TO CRACK.

IN THOSE TIMES WE WILL BE
THE WHISPER WITHIN
SAYING

"IT'S GOING TO BE WORTH IT,

YOUR STORY ISN'T OVER YET."

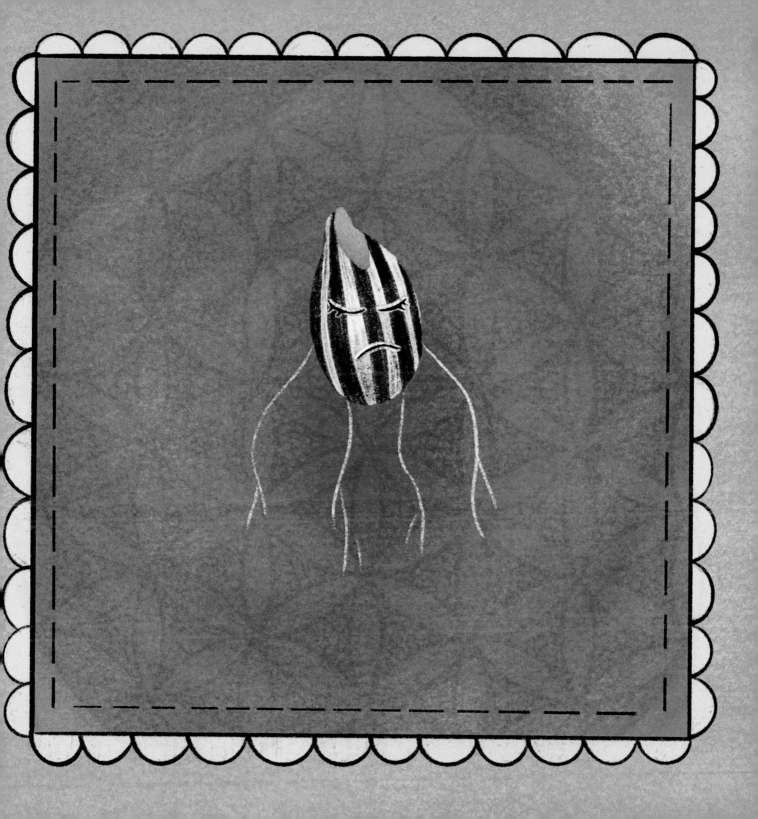

WE WILL ENCOURAGE
YOU TO REACH.
NOT BECAUSE YOU HAVE
ANYTHING TO PROVE,
BUT BECAUSE LIFE
IS A GIFT
WORTH LIVING
TO ITS FULLEST.

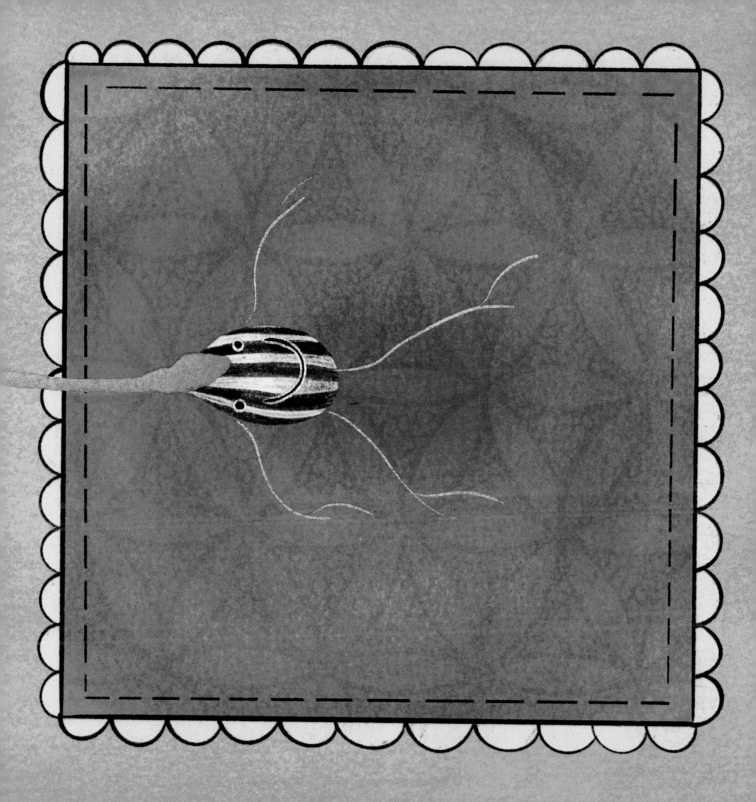

WE WILL CELEBRATE
WITH YOU
ON YOUR
BREAKTHROUGHS—

TEACHING YOU
TO LOOK BACK
WITH GRATITUDE,
AND TO LOOK AHEAD
WITH WONDER
AT ALL OF THE
POSSIBILITIES
YET TO UNFOLD.

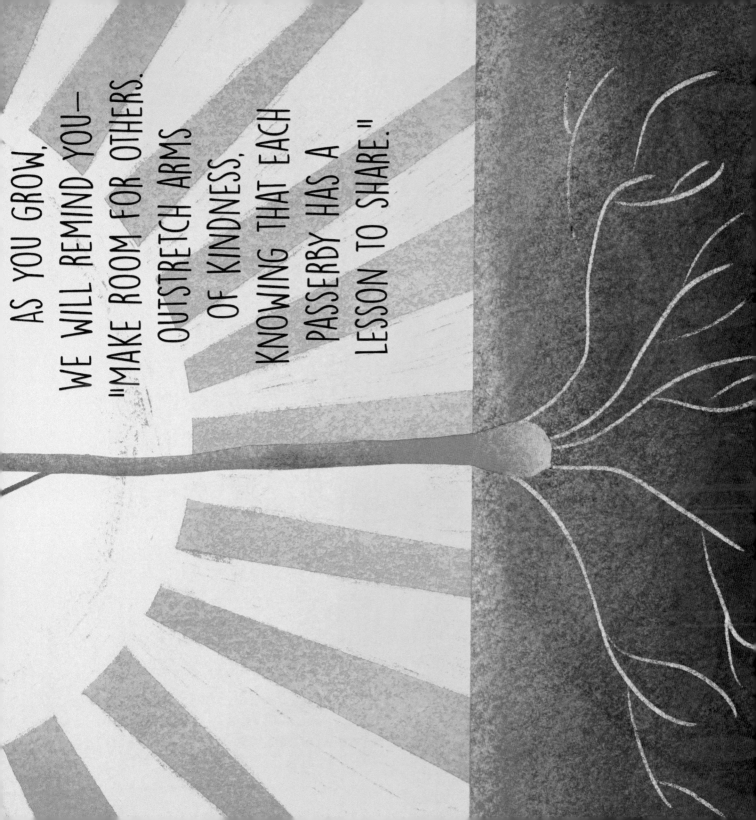

AS YOU GROW,
WE WILL REMIND YOU—
"MAKE ROOM FOR OTHERS.
OUTSTRETCH ARMS
OF KINDNESS,
KNOWING THAT EACH
PASSERBY HAS A
LESSON TO SHARE."

SUNNY, YOU HAVE BEAUTY TO SHARE.

YOU MAY FEEL SHY AND EVEN DOUBT YOURSELF, BUT WHEN THIS HAPPENS BASK IN ALL OF THE LIGHT THAT SURROUNDS YOU...

OPEN UP YOUR PETALS FULLY
TO RECEIVE THE GIFTS
THAT HAVE BEEN GIVEN
TO YOU.
YOU WERE CREATED TO
BLOOM.

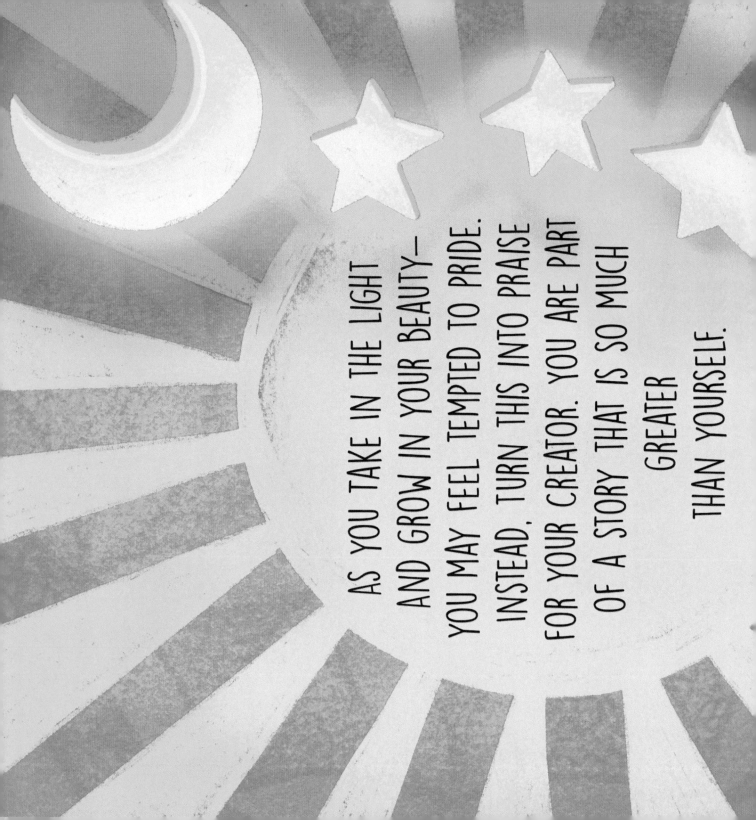

AS YOU TAKE IN THE LIGHT
AND GROW IN YOUR BEAUTY—
YOU MAY FEEL TEMPTED TO PRIDE.
INSTEAD, TURN THIS INTO PRAISE
FOR YOUR CREATOR. YOU ARE PART
OF A STORY THAT IS SO MUCH
GREATER
THAN YOURSELF.

STAY HUMBLE. USE YOUR BEAUTY FOR GOOD. OTHERS TOWARD YOUR SOURCE OF STRENGTH.

SUN UP AND SUN DOWN, YOU CAN POINT
TEACH THEM TO FOLLOW THE LIGHT.

IT MIGHT BE TOO EARLY
TO TELL YOU THIS,
BUT ONE DAY YOUR BEAUTY
WILL FADE.
SOME THINGS ARE TEMPORARY,
SOME ARE ETERNAL.
FAITH, HOPE, AND LOVE
WILL REMAIN.

EVEN WHEN THINGS GROW DARK,
YOU ARE NEVER ALONE.
LOVE SURROUNDS YOU.

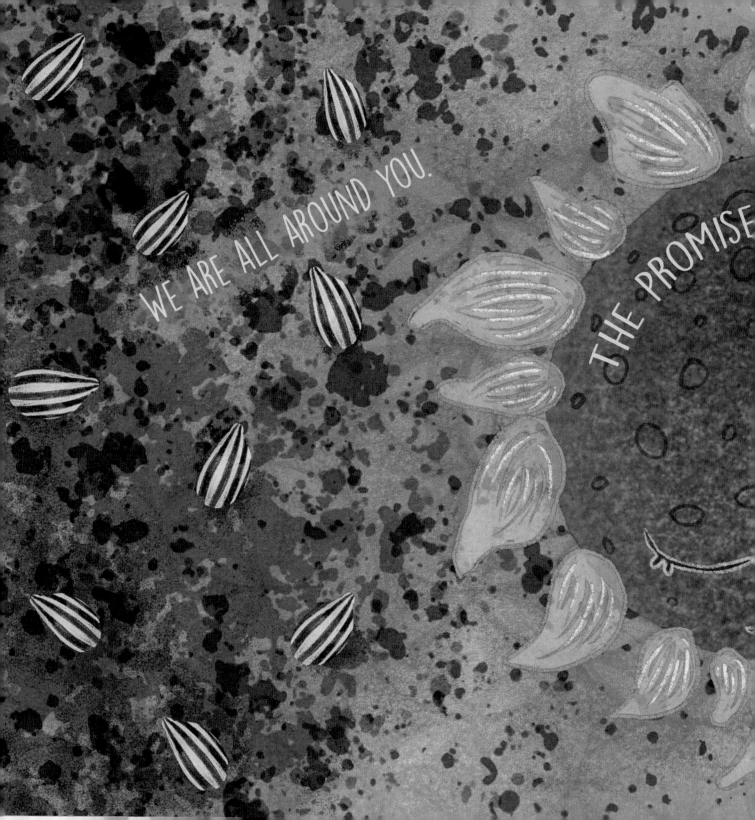

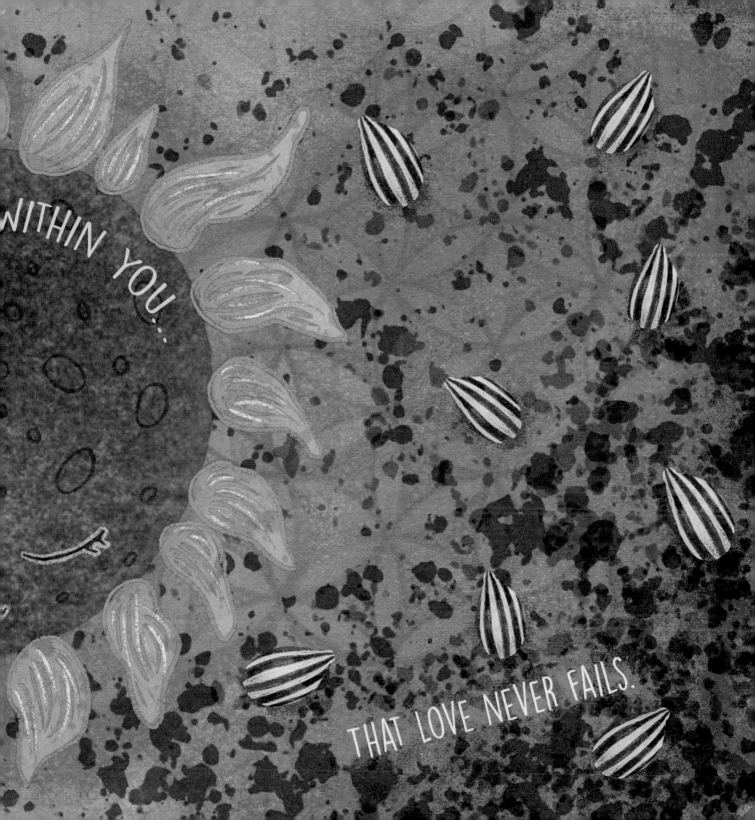

WITHIN YOU...

THAT LOVE NEVER FAILS.

HEY THERE, SUNNY,
WE ARE SO GLAD YOU
ARE HERE.

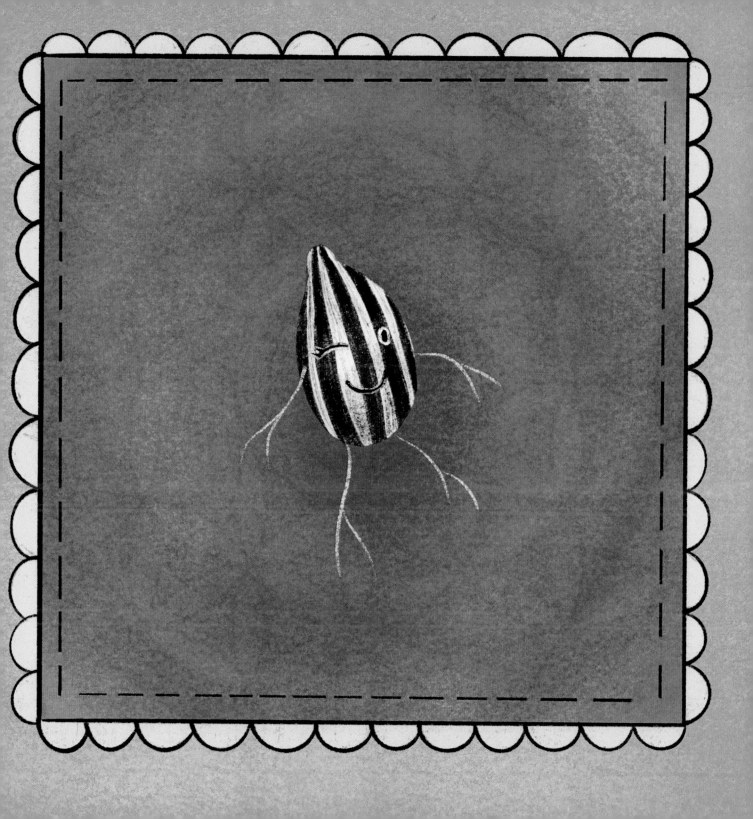

# MOST OF LIFE ON EARTH BEGINS AND ENDS WITH SOIL.

THE HEALTH OF PEOPLE DEPENDS ON THE HEALTH OF PLANTS,
WHICH IN RETURN DEPENDS ON THE HEALTH OF SOIL.
SOIL CONNECTS US ALL IN AN UPWARD SPIRAL OF ABUNDANCE—
AND YET WE HUMANS HAVE BECOME SO DISCONNECTED
FROM THE SCIENCE AND CARE OF THAT WHICH WE DEPEND ON.
SOIL IS SO MUCH MORE THAN DIRT, AND PRESERVING HEALTHY SOIL
FOR FUTURE GENERATIONS DEPENDS ON US.

FOR FUN WAYS THAT YOU CAN JOIN THE MOVEMENT TO PROTECT
AND RENEW THE SOIL, PLEASE VISIT :
WWW.CREATIVEKINDNESSCO.COM

CREATIVEKINDNESSCO.COM

Made in the USA
Coppell, TX
28 March 2022

75667751R00021